Grade K Contents

Get Online!

Letters! An Alphabet Handbook   AC•1–AC•8

Unit 1 Cooperation—All Together Now

How do we live, work, and play together?

Unit 2 Animal and Plant Characteristics—Look at Us!

How are animals and plants unique?

Grade K Contents

Unit 3 Changes—Changes All Around Us

How do changes affect us?

Unit 4 Adventures—Let's Go Exploring

Where will our adventures take us?

PEARSON LANGUAGE CENTRAL

ELD

Consulting Authors

Jim Cummins, Ph.D.

Lily Wong Fillmore, Ph.D.

Georgia García, Ph.D.

Jill Kerper Mora, Ed.D.

PEARSON

Glenview, Illinois • Boston, Massachusetts • Chandler, Arizona • Upper Saddle River, New Jersey

Acknowledgments appear on pages 239–240, which constitute an extension of this copyright page.

ISBN-13: 978-0-328-63432-3
ISBN-10:   0-328-63432-8
12 13 14 15 V011 18 17 16 15

Unit 5 Transportation—Going Places

How do people get from here to there?

Unit 6 Building—Putting It Together

What are different ways of building?

Cooperation— All Together Now

 How do we live, work, and play together?

We Come to School

How do we get to school?

Helping Out

How do people help each other?

Families Help Each Other

How do families cooperate?

Working Together

How do people in a community cooperate?

Fun with Friends

What do you like to do with your friends?

Machines

How do machines help people work together?

Cooperation—All Together Now

Vocabulary

bus

bus stop

driver

school

How do we get to school?

SCHOOL BUS

Picture Dictionary

 **coat**

 **dress**

 **hat**

 **pants**

 **shirt**

 shoes

 Draw Draw things you wear.

✏️ **Circle** Circle *I.*

I am on the bus.

✏️ **Circle** Circle *am.*

I am walking.

Circle Circle the letter.

B   E   B   B   C

D   A   D   C   D

E   E   C   D   E

a   a   b   a   c

c   d   e   c   c

e   e   a   d   e

 **Draw**

Vocabulary

duck

frog

goat

sheep

How do people help each other?

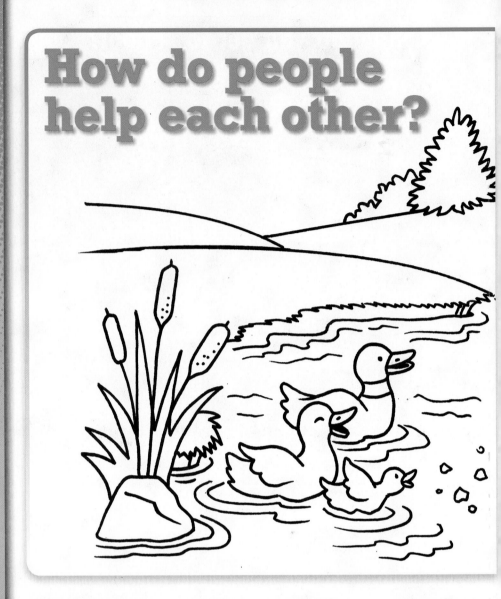

Picture Dictionary

blue　　**green**　　**orange**

purple　　**red**　　**yellow**

✏️ **Circle** Circle red.

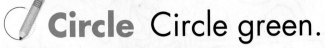

✏️ **Circle** Circle green.

16

✏ **Circle** Circle *I*.

I show my friend how to do things.

✏ **Circle** Circle *am*.

I am sharing.

17

Circle Circle the letter.

G   J   G   N   G

L   I   L   L   K

J   J   N   G   J

F   K   F   F   G

i   i   l   j   i

k   g   k   m   k

h   h   j   h   f

 **Draw**

Vocabulary

grandma

shirt

swing

How do families cooperate?

Picture Dictionary

up

down

in

out

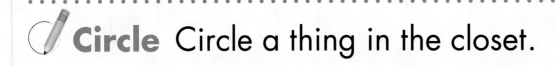

✏️ **Circle** Circle a thing in the closet.

 **Draw**

children

kindergarten

parents

teacher

How do people in a community cooperate?

Shapes

Picture Dictionary

circle

oval

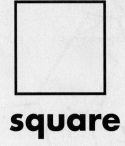

square

triangle

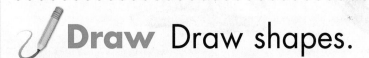

Draw Draw shapes.

28

✏️ **Circle** Circle *the.*

We share the crayons.

✏️ **Circle** Circle *little.*

I listen to my little brother.

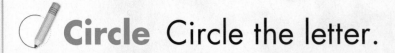

Circle Circle the letter.

Z   T   Z   X   Z

W   W   U   W   Y

T   V   T   T   X

y   w   y   t   y

u   u   u   x   z

v   y   v   w   v

Draw

Vocabulary

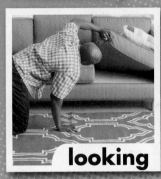

looking

morning

night

find

What do you like to do with your friends?

Picture Dictionary

drums

flute

guitar

piano

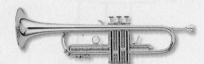

trumpet

violin

 Circle Circle musical instruments.

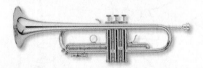

34

✏️ **Circle** Circle *a*.

We fly a kite.

✏️ **Circle** Circle *to*.

We go to the park.

Color Color pictures with /m/.

 **Draw**

fire engines

helicopters

machines

trucks

How do machines help people work together?

39

Picture Dictionary

crane

dump truck

road roller

tractor

 Draw Draw a machine.

✏️ **Circle** Circle *a*.

Food grows on a farm.

✏️ **Circle** Circle *to*.

Trucks take the food to a store.

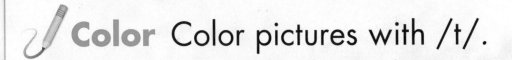 **Color** Color pictures with /t/.

Draw

Get
Online!

Hear it!
See it!
Do it!

- Big Question Video
- Concept Talk Video
- Envision It! Animation
- Grammar Jammer

Animal and Plant Characteristics— Look at Us!

 How are animals and plants unique?

Flowers
How are flowers unique?

Animals Dig
Why do animals dig?

Animals in the Grasslands
What kind of animals live in the grasslands?

Bears Hibernate
Where does a bear hibernate?

Animal Homes
What kind of home does an animal need?

Animals Move
How do animals move?

Animal and Plant Characteristics—Look at Us!

flowers

plants

grow

inside

How are flowers unique?

46

Picture Dictionary

carnation

daisy

lily

rose

sunflower

tulip

 Draw Draw a flower.

Circle Circle *have.*

Flowers have petals.

Circle Circle *is.*

The rose is red.

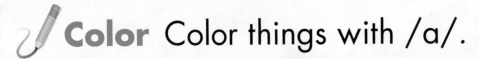 **Color** Color things with /a/.

 **Draw**

Animals Dig

Vocabulary

home

honeybees

neighbors

orange

Why do animals dig?

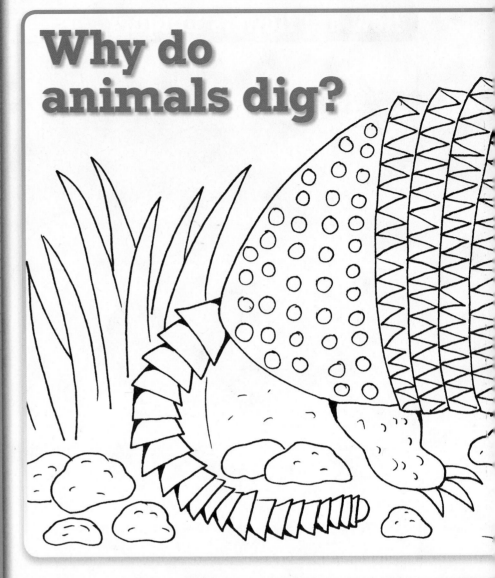

Picture Dictionary

apple

banana

grapes

orange

pear

watermelon

 Draw Draw fruit.

Circle Circle *have*.
Armadillos have claws to dig.

Circle Circle *is*.
An armadillo is digging.

✏️ **Color** Color pictures with /s/.

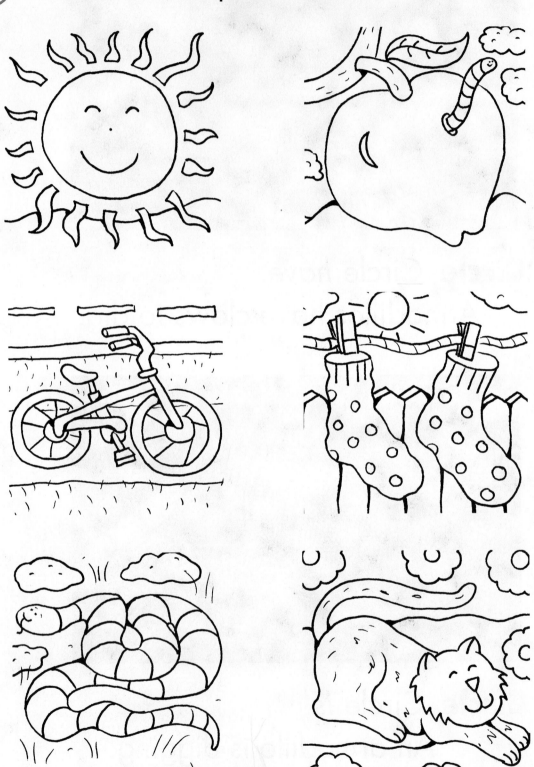

 **Draw**

Animals in the Grasslands

Vocabulary

giraffe

kangaroo

lion

zebra

What kind of animals live in the grasslands?

59

Picture Dictionary

chick

colt

kitten

lamb

piglet

puppy

 Match Match babies with adults.

✏️ **Circle** Circle *We*.

We saw the pups play.

✏️ **Circle** Circle *my*.

Prairie dogs are my favorite animal.

✏️ **Circle** Circle *like*.

I like prairie dogs.

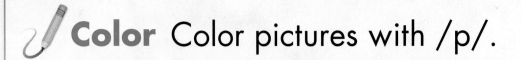 **Color** Color pictures with /p/.

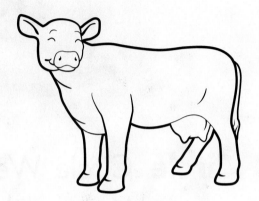

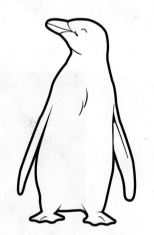
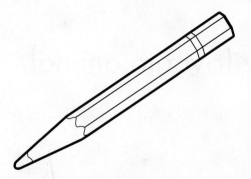

 **Draw**

Vocabulary

bear

snores

Where does a bear hibernate?

Picture Dictionary

den

hive

hole

log

nest

tree

 Draw Draw an animal home.

✏️ **Circle** Circle *We.*

    We saw a bear in a cave.

✏️ **Circle** Circle *my.*

    Bears are my favorite animal.

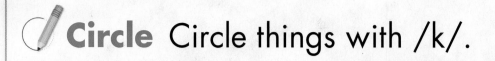 **Circle** Circle things with /k/.

 **Draw**

bed

burrow

cave

winter

What kind of home does an animal need?

burrow

71

Picture Dictionary

top ➡

bottom ➡

over ⬇

under ⬆

🖊 **Circle** Circle the top of the cave.

🖊 **Circle** Circle the frog over the log.

Circle Circle *He.*

He saw a dormouse sleeping.

Circle Circle *for.*

Chipmunks build homes for winter.

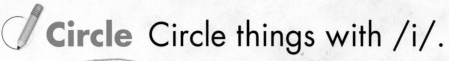 **Circle** Circle things with /i/.

Draw

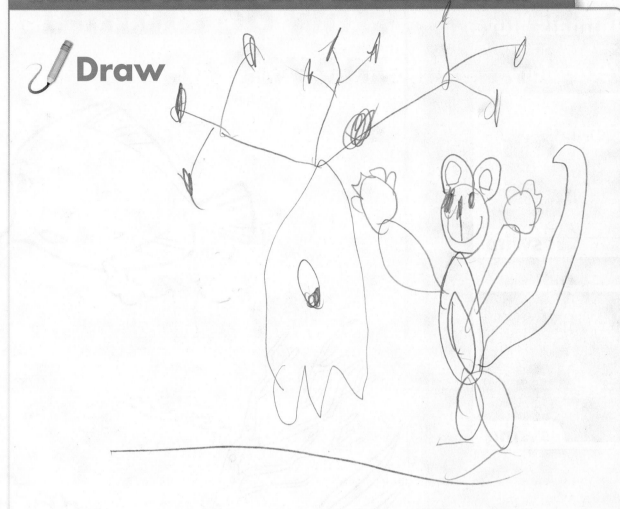

75

swim

swing

How do animals move?

Animals Move

Picture Dictionary

climb

hop

jump

run

skip

walk

 Draw Draw a way to move.

🖊️ **Circle** Circle *He.*

He saw a fox dig a hole.

🖊️ **Circle** Circle *for.*

Meerkats dig for food.

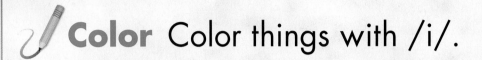 **Color** Color things with /i/.

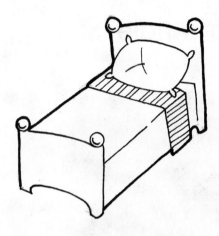

 **Draw**

Hear it!
See it!
Do it!

- Big Question Video
- Concept Talk Video
- Envision It! Animation
- Grammar Jammer

Changes—Changes All Around Us

How do changes affect us?

Unit 3

Moving Away
What happens when a friend moves away?

Getting Older
What new things can you do as you get older?

American Heroes
What can we learn from people in the past?

Friends Change
How do friendships change?

Things Change
How was the past different from today?

Feelings Change
How can we change the way we feel?

Changes—Changes All Around Us

Vocabulary

called

play

shared

word

What happens when a friend moves away?

Picture Dictionary

grandpa   **father**

grandma ➤  ◄ **mother**

sister   **brother**

 Draw Draw your family.

Circle Circle *She*. Circle *me*.
She told me good-bye.

Circle Circle *with*.
I cannot play with my friend.

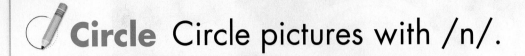 **Circle** Circle pictures with /n/.

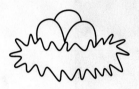 

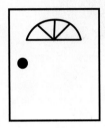  

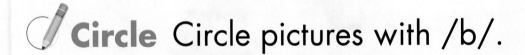 **Circle** Circle pictures with /b/.

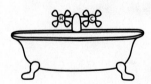  

 **Draw**

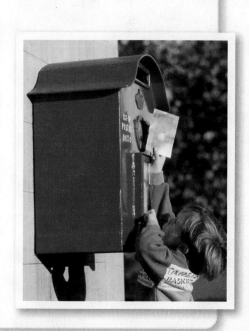

Vocabulary

duck

water

What new things can you do as you get older?

Picture Dictionary

happy

sad

scared

excited

 Draw Draw feelings.

happy	**sad**

✏️ **Circle** Circle *with*. Circle *me*.
You ride with me.

✏️ **Circle** Circle *She*.
She rides without help.

Color Color pictures with /r/.

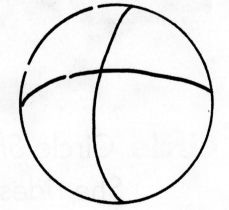

 **Draw**

Vocabulary

crowds

hero

sign

storm

What can we learn from people in the past?

Picture Dictionary

bell

blacksmith

cottage

horse

 Circle Circle things in a Colonial village.

98

✏️ **Circle** Circle *see*.

I see Lincoln's hat.

✏️ **Circle** Circle *Look*.

Look at Ben Franklin work.

Circle Circle pictures with /d/.

 Circle Circle pictures with /k/.

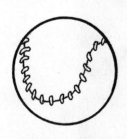 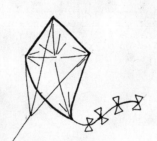 

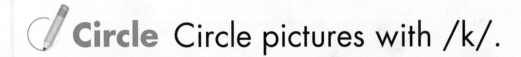

 Draw

friends

game

How do friendships change?

Picture Dictionary

feathers

fur

quills

scales

shell

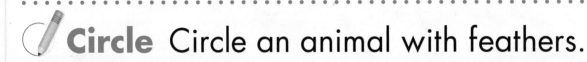

Circle Circle an animal with feathers.

Circle Circle an animal with a shell.

✏️ **Circle** Circle *see.*

I see my friend after school.

✏️ **Circle** Circle *Look.*

Look at the friends playing.

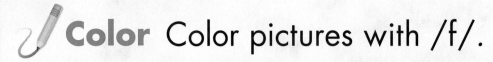 **Color** Color pictures with /f/.

 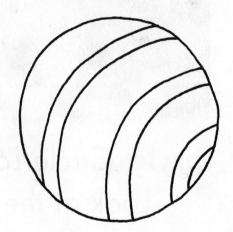

 **Draw**

camera

news

How was the past different from today?

Picture Dictionary

book

calendar

crayons

desk

paper

pencil

 Draw Draw things in a classroom.

🖊 **Circle** Circle *They*.

They were in one classroom.

🖊 **Circle** Circle *you*.

Today you can use a computer.

🖊 **Circle** Circle *of*.

All of us go to school now.

Color Color things with /o/.

 **Draw**

Feelings Change

Vocabulary

roar

strong

How can we change the way we feel?

114

Picture Dictionary

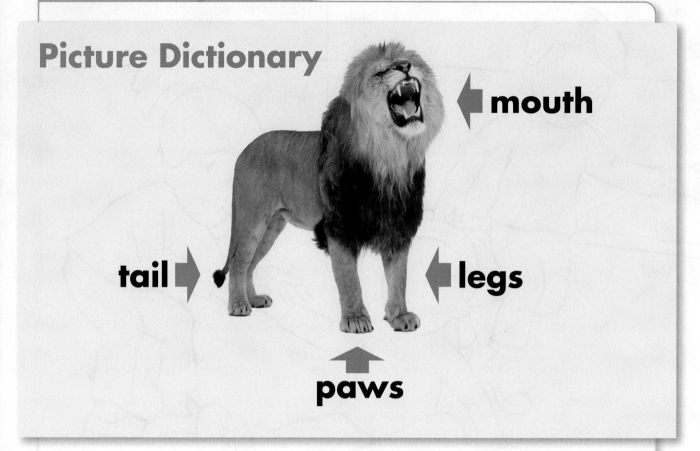

mouth

tail

legs

paws

· ·

Circle Circle the tail.

· ·

Circle Circle a paw.

116

✏️ **Circle** Circle *They.*
   They were good friends.

✏️ **Circle** Circle *you.* Circle *of.*
   Friends take care of you.

Circle Circle things with /o/.

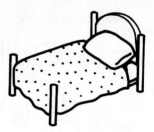

 **Draw**

Adventures—
Let's Go Exploring

 Where will our adventures take us?

A Day's Adventures
What adventures can you have every day?

A Lucky Day
What adventures can you have on a lucky day?

Animal Adventures
What adventures can animals have?

Goldilocks's Adventures
What kind of adventures can a child have?

Cold Adventures
What is it like in the Antarctic?

City Adventures
What are some city adventures?

Adventures—Let's Go Exploring

Vocabulary

bunnies

clock

nap

play

rabbit

What adventures can you have every day?

123

Picture Dictionary

cereal

eggs

toast

waffles

 Draw Draw breakfast foods.

✏️ **Circle** Circle *are*.

We are happy to have a class pet.

✏️ **Circle** Circle *do*. Circle *that*.

We do projects that are fun.

Color Color things with /h/.

 **Draw**

bath

dinner

rabbit

What adventures can you have on a lucky day?

Picture Dictionary

pizza

salad

sandwich

soup

spaghetti

stew

 Draw Draw dinner foods.

Circle Circle *are.* Circle *do.*

We do things that are special.

Circle Circle *That.*

That is lucky!

Color Color things with /l/.

Draw

cottontails

mouse

snakes

squirrels

frogs

What adventures can animals have?

135

Picture Dictionary

small

large

short

tall

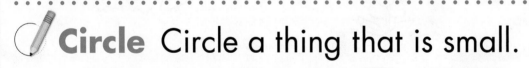

Circle Circle a thing that is small.

Circle Circle a thing that is tall.

Circle Circle *One.* Circle *two.*
One squirrel will eat two acorns.

Circle Circle *Three.*
Three birds live in the tree.

Circle Circle *Four.* Circle *five.*
Four or five birds can live in the tree.

Circle Circle the beginning sounds.

   /tr/   /kr/

   /sp/   /sk/

 Circle Circle the ending sounds.

   /nd/   /ft/

   /st/   /sk/

 **Draw**

baby

father

mother

woods

What kind of adventures can a child have?

Picture Dictionary

bed

chair

table

dresser

 Draw Draw furniture.

Circle Circle *One*. Circle *three*.
One girl visited three bears.

Circle Circle *two*.
She saw two squirrels in the woods.

Circle Circle *four*. Circle *five*.
She saw four or five birds.

Circle Circle things with /g/.

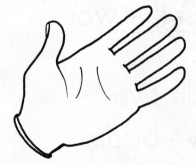

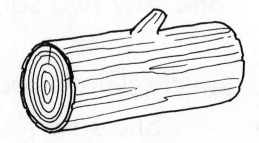

Draw

Cold Adventures

Vocabulary

penguin

ship

sled

thunder

What is it like in the Antarctic?

Penguin.

Ship.

147

Picture Dictionary

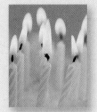

hot

cold

warm

freezing

 Match Match temperatures.

cold

hot

🖊 **Circle** Circle *from*. Circle *here*.
　　　　Start sledding from here.

🖊 **Circle** Circle *go*.
　　　　Penguins go sledding too.

Color Color things with /e/.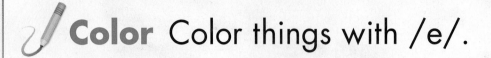

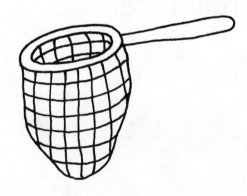

 **Draw**

bread

grandma

park

What are some city adventures?

153

Picture Dictionary

clouds

moon

stars

sun

 Draw Draw things in the sky.

✏️ **Circle** Circle *Here.*

Here is the city market.

✏️ **Circle** Circle *Go.* Circle *from.*

Go from the museum to the park.

Circle Circle things with /e/.

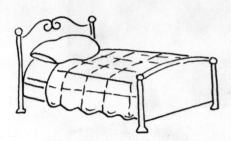

What are some city adventures?

 **Draw**

Transportation— Going Places

THE BIG ?

How do people get from here to there?

Unit 5

Getting Places
What are some forms of transportation?

Help in an Emergency
What kinds of transportation help us in an emergency?

Going Places at Work
How does transportation help at work?

Trains
How does a train get over a mountain?

Ways to Travel
How do people around the world travel?

Ways to Get to School
How do children get to school?

bus

train

What are some forms of transportation?

Picture Dictionary

boat

car

train

truck

 Draw Draw a kind of transportation.

✏️ **Circle** Circle *yellow*.
The plane was near a yellow line.

✏️ **Circle** Circle *green*. Circle *blue*.
A green plane flew in the blue sky.

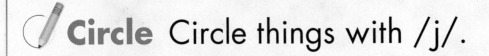

Circle Circle things with /j/.

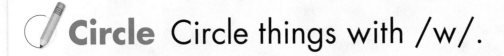

Circle Circle things with /w/.

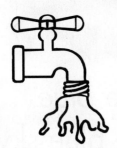

Draw

Vocabulary

boat

swimmer

taxi

What kinds of transportation help us in an emergency?

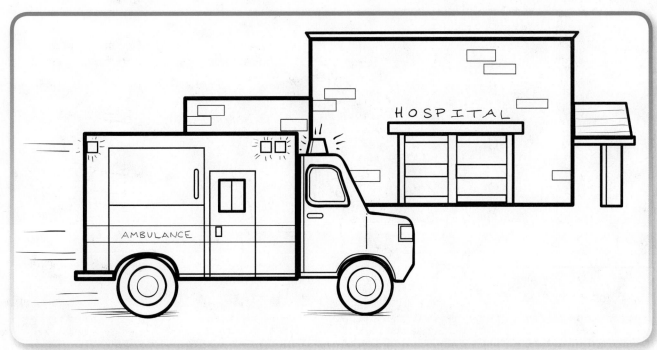

Picture Dictionary

Coast Guard

firefighters

nurse

police

 Draw Draw someone who helps us.

Circle Circle *yellow*. Circle *blue*.
A yellow boat was in the blue water.

Circle Circle *green*.
They saved a green turtle.

✏️ **Circle** Circle things with /ks/.

Draw

Vocabulary

parking lots

rain

tunnels

bike

snow

sun

wind

How does transportation help at work?

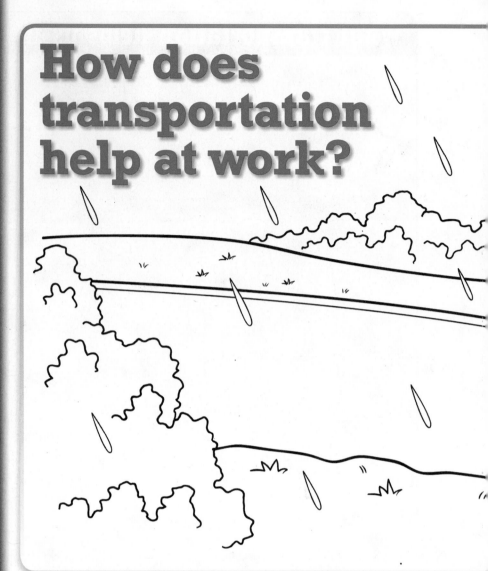

mail truck

173

Picture Dictionary

astronaut

bike messenger

cashier

mechanic

teacher

writer

 Draw Draw someone doing a job.

✏ **Circle** Circle *what.*

The messenger knows what to wear.

✏ **Circle** Circle *said.* Circle *was.*

He said the mask was warm.

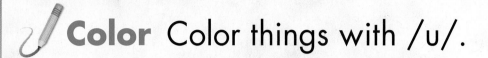

Color Color things with /u/.

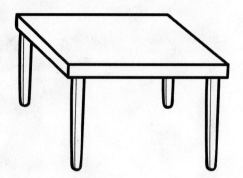

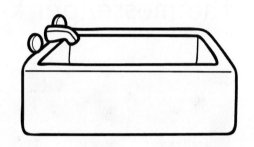

 **Draw**

dining cars

dolls

sleeping cars

load
switching
toys
wheels

How does a train get over a mountain?

Picture Dictionary

ball

blocks

doll

puzzle

stuffed animal

top

Draw Draw toys.

✏️ **Circle** Circle *said*. Circle *what*.
The little engine said what it could do.

✏️ **Circle** Circle *was*.
The little engine was trying hard.

Circle Circle things with /u/.

Draw

airplane

camel

ocean

trail

air   land

water

How do people around the world travel?

185

Picture Dictionary

desert

lake

mountain

river

volcano

waterfall

 Draw Draw a place in the world.

Circle Circle *where.*

The driver knew where to go.

Circle Circle *Come.*

Come see the town.

✏️ **Circle** Circle things with /v/.

✏️ **Circle** Circle things with /z/.

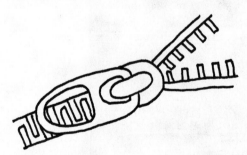

Draw

Ways to Get to School

Vocabulary

bicycles

radio

train

bus

car

school

How do children get to school?

Picture Dictionary

countryside

farm

town

village

 Draw Draw a place to live.

Circle Circle *where*.

The yak goes where she goes.

Circle Circle *come*.

We come to school.

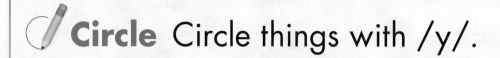

✏ **Circle** Circle things with /y/.

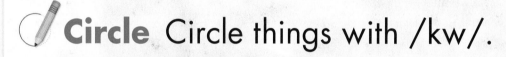

✏ **Circle** Circle things with /kw/.

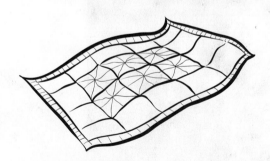
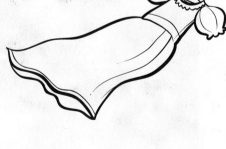

 **Draw**

Get Online!

Hear it!
See it!
Do it!

- Big Question Video
- Concept Talk Video
- Envision It! Animation
- Grammar Jammer

Building—Putting It Together

What are different ways of building?

Unit 6

Building a School
What do you need to build a school?

Tools for Building
What tools do you need to build things?

Busy Beavers
How do beavers build?

Night Workers
Who works at night?

Building a House
Who helps to build a house?

Ants' Nests
How do ants build?

Building—Putting It Together

pipes

spills

wires

What do you need to build a school?

199

Picture Dictionary

bricks

cement

steel

wood

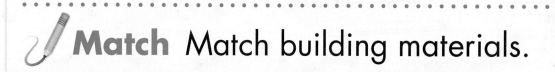

Match Match building materials.

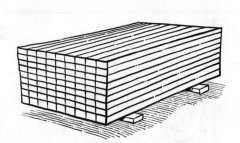

✏️ **Circle** Circle *He*. Circle *a*. Circle *to*.
He uses a bulldozer to move dirt.

✏️ **Circle** Circle *Look*. Circle *the*. Circle *go*.
Look at the truck go!

✏️ **Circle** Circle things with /a/.

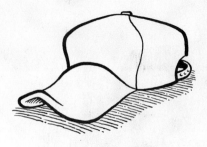

✏️ **Circle** Circle things with /i/.

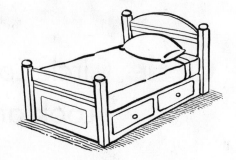

 **Draw**

What do you need to build a school?

cat

cow

goat

dog

mouse

rooster

sheep

What tools do you need to build things?

205

Picture Dictionary

cow

goat

rooster

sheep

 Draw Draw a farm animal.

✏️ **Circle** Circle *We*. Circle *are*.
We are making a house.

✏️ **Circle** Circle *Here*. Circle *is*.
Here is the hammer.

Circle Circle things with /o/.

 Draw

kits

mud

pond

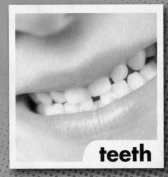

teeth

trees

How do beavers build?

Picture Dictionary

grass

leaves

mud

sticks

 Circle Circle what animals use.

✏️ **Circle** Circle *Two*.

Two beavers are swimming.

✏️ **Circle** Circle *They*. Circle *have*.

They have homes on the water.

Circle Circle things with /e/.

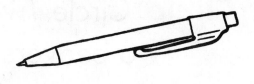

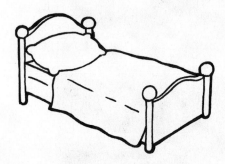

How do beavers build?

 **Draw**

delivery worker

machinery

policewoman

Who works at night?

Delivery Express

Picture Dictionary

 **bulldozer**

 **cement mixer**

 **concrete**

 **crane**

 **goggles**

 **hard hat**

 Draw Draw something at a site.

Circle Circle *do*. Circle *that*.
A crane can do that.

Circle Circle *I*. Circle *like*. Circle *see*.
I like to see big trucks.

Circle Circle things with /u/.

✎ **Draw**

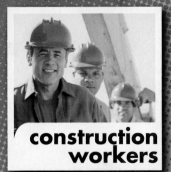

**construction
workers**

neighbors

truck driver

Who helps to build a house?

Picture Dictionary

apartment

house

hut

igloo

teepee

trailer

 Draw Draw a home.

✏ **Circle** Circle *Four*.
Four workers built a wall.

✏ **Circle** Circle *She*. Circle *was*.
She was laying bricks.

Match Match words with pictures.

bed

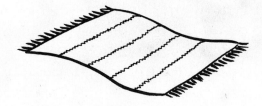

hat

log

rug

pig

Draw

ant

fall

spring

hundreds

months

How do ants build?

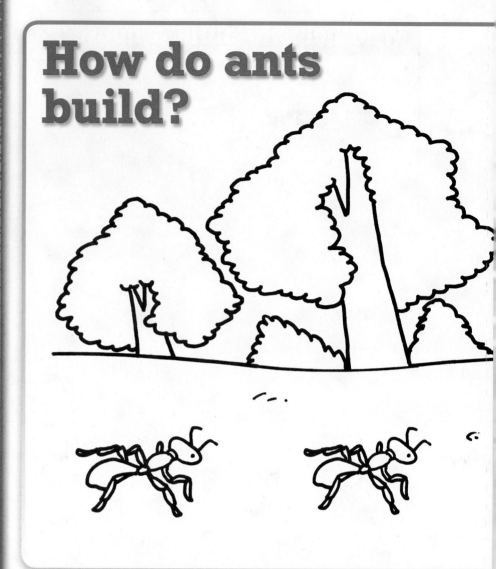

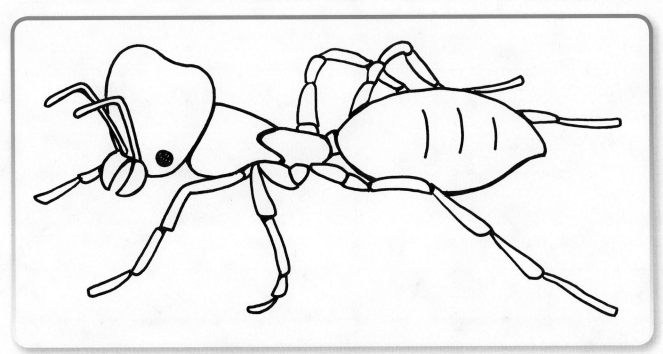

Picture Dictionary

bee

beetle

cricket

wasp

 Draw Draw an insect.

✏️ **Circle** Circle *come*.

Worker ants come to dig tunnels.

✏️ **Circle** Circle *One*.

One queen ant lays eggs.

Match Match words with pictures.

 **ant**

 **cup**

 **hen**

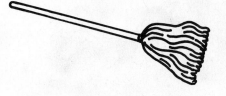 **pig**

 **mop**

Draw

Picture Glossary

Colors

blue	orange	red
green	purple	yellow

Numbers

1	one	
2	two	
3	three	
4	four	
5	five	
6	six	
7	seven	
8	eight	
9	nine	
10	ten	

Clothing

dress	**hat**	**pants**
shoes	**shorts**	**t-shirt**

Weather

 **jacket**	**raincoat**	 **rainy**
 **snowy**	**sunny**	 **umbrella**

Family

sister   **brother**

mother

 Ana **father**

grandmother   **grandfather**

Picture Glossary

address

bathroom

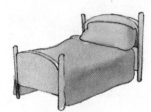
bed

bedroom

couch

dining room

door

house

kitchen

living room

oven

phone

room

window

tub

adding

book

chair

crayon

desk

globe

map

painting

pencil

reading

story

table

working on the computer

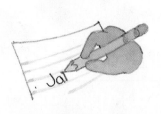

writing

Credits

Illustrations

8, 114, 160, 228 Marilyn Janovitz; 14, 108, 204 Donna Bizjak; 20, 32 Liisa Guida; 26, 76, 96 Wednesday Kirwan; 38, 64 Ann Iosa; 46, 70, 102, 146, 184 Anette Heiberg; 52, 128 Diane Greenseid; 58 David Preiss; 84 Jane Smith; 90, 152 Sharon Vargo; 122, 134 Sarah Beise; 140 Janet McDonnell; 166, 190 Dani Jones; 172, 216 Deb Johnson; 178 Scott Rolf; 198 Robbie Short; 210, 222 Liz Goulet Dubois

Photographs

Every effort has been made to secure permission and provide appropriate credit for photographic material. The publisher deeply regrets any omission and pledges to correct errors called to its attention in subsequent editions.

Unless otherwise acknowledged, all photographs are the property of Pearson Education, Inc.

Photo locators denoted as follows: Top (T), Center (C), Bottom (B), Left (L), Right (R), Background (Bkgd).

2 ©Douglas Menuez/Riser/Getty Images; 6 (A) Hallgerd/Shutterstock; 8 (CL) ©Matt Henry Gunther/Getty Images, (TL) dzain/Fotolia, (CL) ©Purestock/Alamy, (BL) brianguest/Fotolia; 10 (TR) Howard Shooter/©DK Images, (TL, BL, BC, BR) Getty Images, (TC) ©Jana Leon/ Getty Images; 11 (T) Getty Images, (B) ©Design Pics Inc./Alamy; 13 ©Jupiter Images/Creatas/Alamy; 14 (TL) ©Jupiter Images/Creatas/ Alamy, (TL) Geoff Dann/©DK Images, (TL) Dave King/©DK Images, (TL) Peter Chadwick/©DK Images; 16 (CL) Getty Images, (CR) ©Westend61/Getty Images, (CR) ©Corbis/Jupiter Images, (BL) Dave King/©DK Images; 17 (B) ©JLP/Jose L. Pelaez/Corbis, (T) ©Alexander Nicholson/Photonica/Getty Images; 19 ©Corbis Super RF/Alamy; 20 Getty Images; 22 (CL) ©D. Hurst/Alamy Images, (CR) ©Jupiter Images/Polka Dot/Alamy, (TL) ©Matt Gray/Taxi/Getty Images, (TR) ©Matt Carr/Photonica/Getty Images; 23 (T) ©MIXA Co., Ltd./Alamy, (B) ©Lauren Burke/Getty Images; 25 ©Blend Images/Getty Images; 26 (TL) ©VCL/Spencer Rowell/Getty Images, (TL) ©Martin Riedl/Getty Images, (TL) ©Alex Mares-Manton/Asia Images/Getty Images, (TL) Getty Images; 29 (B) ©blue jean images/Getty Images, (T) Getty Images; 31 ©age fotostock/SuperStock; 32 (TL) ©Suk-Heui Park/Photographer's Choice/Getty Images, (TL) Getty Images, (TL) ©Corbis/Jupiter Images; 34 (TL, TCL, TCR) Dave King/©DK Images, (TC) Philip Dowell/©DK Images, (TR, TC) ©DK Images; 35 (B) ©Steve Satushek/Getty Images, (T) ©Hallgerd/Shutterstock; 37 ©Kevin Dodge/Corbis; 38 (TL) ©Johnny Greig/Alamy Images, (TL) ©Dorothy Young Riess M.D./Workbook Stock/Jupiter Images, (TL) ©Jupiter Images/Comstock Images/Alamy, (TL) ©George Hall/ Corbis, (TL) Lynton Gardiner/©DK Images; 40 (TL) ©Tetra Images/Alamy, (TCL) Mike Dunning/©DK Images, (TCR) Richard Leeney/©DK Images, (CL) ©Construction Photography/Corbis; 41 (T) Jupiter Images, (B) ©Jim West/Alamy Images; 43 ©Ian Shaw/Alamy Images; 46 (TL) ©William Manning/Corbis, (TL) ©Tim Street-Porter/Beateworks/Corbis; 48 (CC) Getty Images, (TR) Roger Smith/©DK Images, (TC) Craig Knowles/©DK Images, (TCL) Clive Boursnell/©DK Images, (TR) ©DEA/F. Luccese/De Agostini Picture Library/Getty Images, (CR) ©Frans Lemmens/Iconica/Getty Images; 49 (B) ©Corbis Premium RF/Alamy, (T) Steve Gorton/©DK Images; 51 ©Martin Brigdale/ Dorling Kindersley/Getty Images; 52 (TL) ©Cydney Conger/Corbis, (TL) ©Hans Reinhard/zefa/Corbis, (TL) ©Ariel Skelley/Corbis, (TL) Tim Ridley/©DK Images; 54 (TC, TCR) Getty Images, (TL, CC) ©DK Images, (TCL) Tim Ridley/©DK Images; 55 (TC) Arto Hakola/ Shutterstock, (BC) ©Steve Bower/ Shutterstock; 57 ©Claudia Adams/Alamy Images; 58 (TL) ©J & B Photographers/Animals Animals/ Earth Scenes, (TL) ©Roger De La Harpe/Animals Animals/Earth Scenes, (TL) Getty Images, (TL) ©DK Images; 60 (TL) Jane Burton/©DK Images, (CC) Gordon Clayton/©DK Images, (TCL) ©DK Images, (CC) Bill Ling/©DK Images, (CR) ©Pat Doyle/Corbis; 61 (TC) Henk Bentlage/Shutterstock, (BC) ©Jorg & Petra Wegner/Animals Animals/Earth Scenes; 63 ©Art Wolfe/Getty Images; 64 ©Henry King/ Photonica/Getty Images; 66 (TL) ©Phyllis Greenberg/Animals Animals/Earth Scenes, (TC) Ken Preston-Mafham/Animals Animals/Earth Scenes, (CC) ©Richard Day/Animals Animals/Earth Scenes, (CR) ©Kevin Schafer/Corbis, (CL) Thinkstock, (TR) ©Edwin Giesbers/Foto Natura/Getty Images; 67 (TC) Malcolm McGregor/DK Images, (BC) ©Suzi Eszterhas/Animals Animals/Earth Scenes; 69 ©Tom J. Ulrich/ Visuals Unlimited; 70 (TL) ©A & M Shah/Animals Animals/Earth Scenes, (TL) ©E. Bartov/OSF/Animals Animals/Earth Scenes, (TL) ©Craig Tuttle/Corbis, (TL) Ray Moller/©DK Images; 72 (TL) ©Image Source, (TR) ©Larry Dale Gordon/Photographer's Choice/Getty Images; 73 (BC) ©Frank Cezus/Taxi/Getty Images, (TC) ©O. Newman/OSF/Animals Animals/Earth Scenes; 75 ©Joe McDonald/Corbis; 76 (TL) ©DLILLC/Corbis, (TL) ©Mike Powell/Stone+/Getty Images; 78 (CC) ©Cultura/Alamy, (TCR) ©Design Pics Inc./Alamy, (TR) ©Jupiter Images/Comstock Images/Alamy, (TL) ©Patrick Molnar/The Image Bank/Getty Images, (TC) ©LWA-Dann Tardif/Corbis, (CL) ©David Stoecklein/Corbis; 79 (TC) ©Joe McDonald/Animals Animals/Earth Scenes, (BC) ©Ana Laura Gozalez/Animals Animals/Earth Scenes; 81 ©Renee Lynn/Corbis; 84 (TL) ©Norbert Schaefer/Corbis, (TL) ©Image100/Jupiter Images, (TL) ©Tomas Rodriguez/Solas Photography/Veer, Inc.; 86 ©Jupiter Images/Brand X/Alamy; 87 (B) Corbis, (T) ©Jupiter Images/Brand X/Alamy; 89 Getty Images; 90 (TL) ©Nik Wheeler/Corbis, (TL) ©altrendo nature/Getty Images; 92 (CR) ©Elyse Lewin/Getty Images, (TR) ©Jupiter Images/Brand X/ Alamy, (CR) ©Jupiter Images/BananaStock/Alamy, (TL) ©Donna Day/Corbis; 93 (T) ©Purestock/Alamy, (B) ©Nancy Sheehan/PhotoEdit; 95 ©Blend Images/Alamy; 96 (TL) ©John Lund/Stone/Getty Images, (TL) ©Glow Images/Alamy, (TL) ©Blend Images/Getty Images, (TL) ©Blend Images/Jupiter Images; 98 (TR) ©Lance Burnell/Alamy Images, (TCL) ©David Stuckel/Alamy Images, (TCR) ©Lynn Seldon/ Danita Delimont, Agent, (TL) ©Ron & Patty Thomas/Getty Images; 99 (B) The Granger Collection, NY, (T) ©Scherl/SV-Bilderdienst/The Image Works, Inc.; 101 The Granger Collection, NY; 102 (TL) ©Bob Daemmrich/The Image Works, Inc., (TL) Getty Images; 104 (TC) ©Rick & Nora Bowers/Alamy Images, (TCR) ©Breck P. Kent/Animals Animals/Earth Scenes, (TL) ©Guy Motil/Flirt Photography/Veer, Inc., (TCL) ©Altrendo Nature/Getty Images, (TR) ©Julian Deghy/Alamy Images; 105 (B) Steve Skjold /Alamy Images, (T) Getty Images; 107 ©Simon Marcus/Corbis; 108 (TL) ©Judith Collins/Alamy, (TL) ©Jupiter Images/Brand X/Alamy; 110 (TL) ©Supapixx/Alamy, (TCL) Jupiter Images, (CC) Stockdisc, (TCR) ©Gregor Schuster/Getty Images, (TR) Dave King/©DK Images; 111 (C) ©Rubberball/Punchstock, (B) ©David Pollack/Corbis, (T) The Granger Collection, NY; 113 ©Bettmann/Corbis; 114 (TL) ©Andy Rouse/The Image Bank/Getty

Handbook

Aa Bb Cc Dd Ee Ff Gg Hh Ii Jj Kk Ll Mm
Nn Oo Pp Qq Rr Ss Tt Uu Vv Ww Xx Yy Zz

The Alphabet cards can help you
with sounds in English.

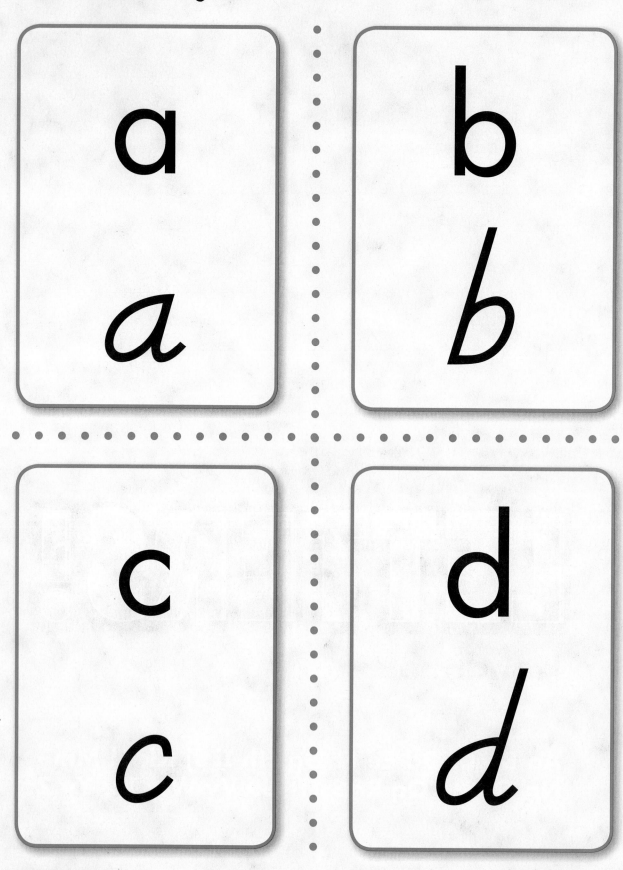

a   a

b   b

c   c

d   d

e

e

f

f

g

g

h

h

i
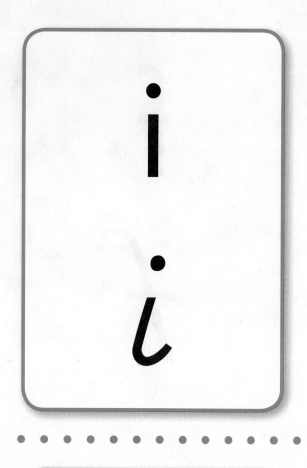

j
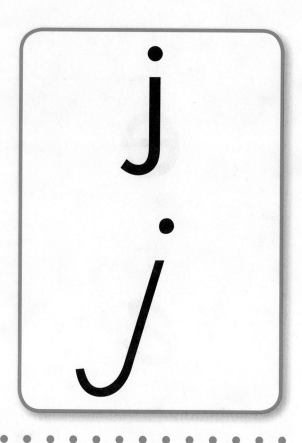

k

l
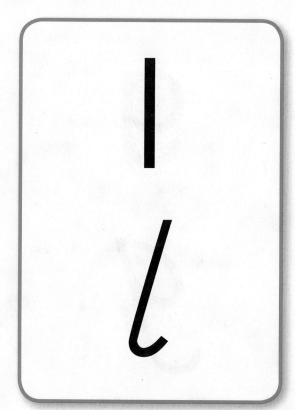

m

m

n

n

o

o

p

p

q

q

r

r

s

s

t

t

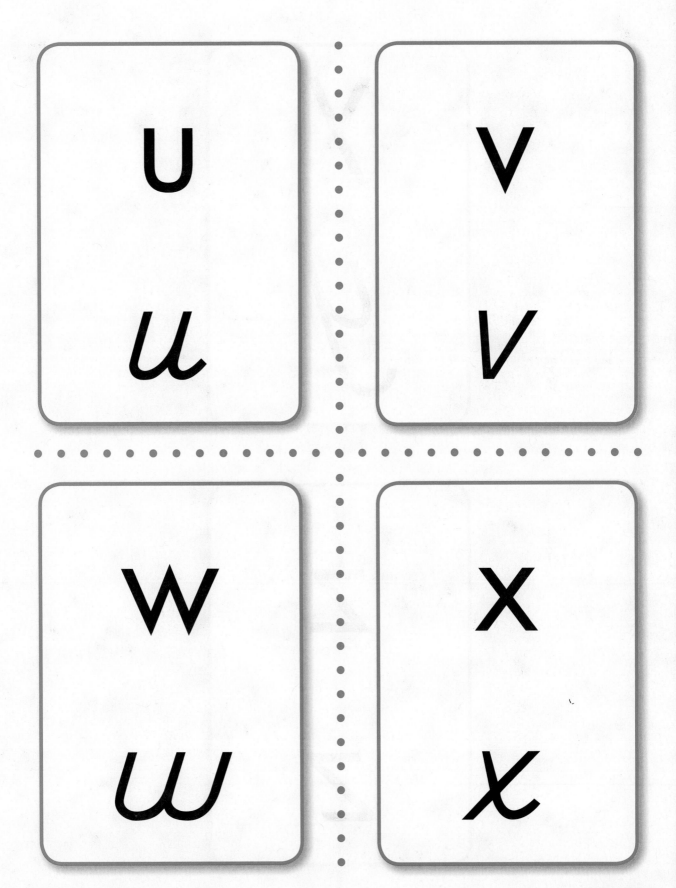

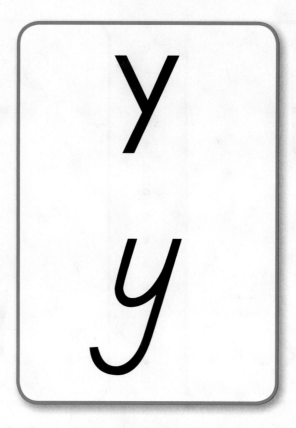

Y y

Z z